MW00788271

ISBN 0-7683-2154-9

Text by Flavia and Lisa Weedn
Illustrations by Flavia Weedn

www.flavia.com

Published in 2000 by Cedco Publishing Company
100 Pelican Way, San Rafael, California 94901
For a free catalog of other Cedco® products, please write
to the address above, or visit our website: www.cedco.com

Printed in Hong Kong
1 3 5 7 9 10 8 6 4 2

The artwork for each picture is digitally mastered using acrylic on canvas.

In this wondrous life,
the bonds of true friendship
are a precious gift.

written by

date

May 13, 2003

Other Flavia Books

Kindred Spirits: Address Book
Forever: Footprints on Our Hearts
Forever: An Illustrated Address Book
Across the Porch from God: Reflections of Gratitude
Across the Porch from God: A Gratitude Journal
To Take Away the Hurt: Insights to Healing
To Take Away the Hurt: A Healing Journal
Heart and Soul: A Personal Tale of Love and Romance
Vows of Love: A Guided Wedding Journal & Planner
Vows of Love: Wedding Guest Register
Heaven and Earth: A Journal of Dreams and Awakenings
Blessings of Motherhood: A Journal of Love
Dear Little One: A Memory Book of Baby's First Year
Passages: A Woman's Personal Journey
Passages: An Address Book for Women

A FRIENDSHIP JOURNAL

Kindred Spirits

Flavia and Lisa Weedn
Illustrated by Flavia Weedn

Cedco Publishing Company • San Rafael, California

Friends are those who take time enough to listen, who share our laughter, tears, and dreams. They know the things we **hope** for and the things we'll never be. They celebrate our joys and our victories. They blanket us with care when we need them most. It is a **miracle** of fate that through the maze of a million faces, we manage to find soul mates along the way – **kindred spirits** who understand our thoughts and share the same passion and glory of this lifetime.

Friends recognize the bright spirit within us

and help us to see it within ourselves.

They are mirrors to our souls

and champions of understanding.

Lucky are we who know the blessing of true friendship,

for it encourages us to become all we are meant to be.

This journal is designed to record your thoughts,

your feelings, and your memories.

May it be a private celebration

of those who matter in your life.

Close to My Heart

Somehow, within the mystery of life, we met. And now,
because we are friends, how very blessed am I.

Beautiful people cause beautiful things to happen.

The discovery of a kindred soul is one of life's finest treasures.

"And what is as important as knowledge?" asked the mind.
"Caring and seeing with heart," answered the soul.

Joy, needing to be heard, always finds its way to a friend.

Friendship nurtures the child's heart within us.

Shared Moments

The heart of humanity is found
in the little-known kindnesses of others.

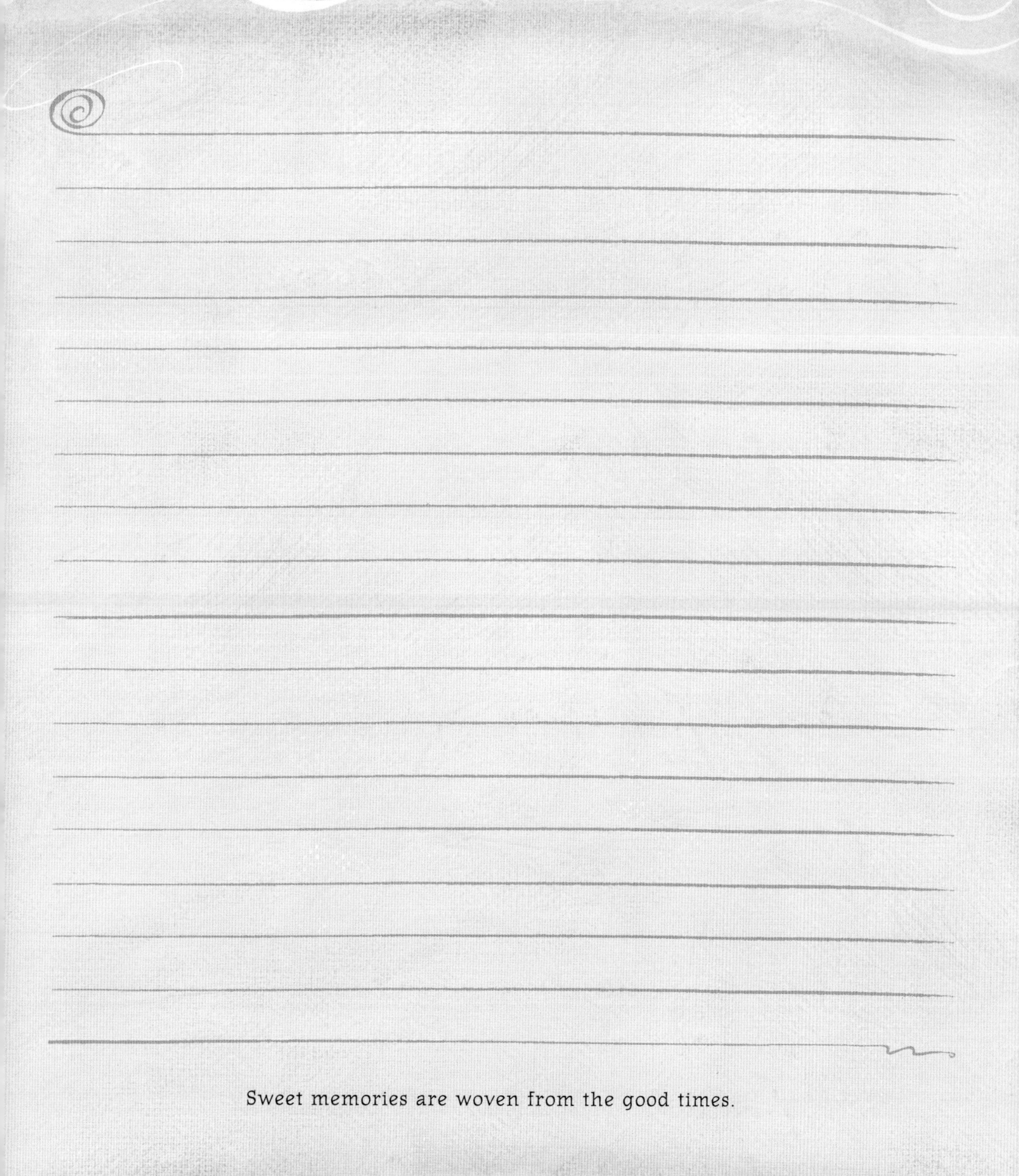

Sweet memories are woven from the good times.

One of my favorite things is the pleasure of your company.
Shared laughter and stolen moments have given my spirit wings.

Time is a miracle and life is a gift. Remember everything.

To those who matter in our life,
time is the most valuable gift we can give.

When we offer a listening heart,
we give our loved ones a safe place to rest.

Soul Mates
RAINBOWS
GLORY

FREESIA
25¢
BULBS

What a wondrous gift of fate that we could
live our lives at the same time on earth.

So many of my dreams and the things
I feel inside my heart are there because of you.

Real friends help us remember
who we are and all we yearn to be.

Friends are timeless mirrors who reflect our higher selves.

If I could sit across the porch from God,
I'd thank Him for lending me you.

The world knows little of its greatest heroes.

Love & Care

SUNSHINE AND WATER

LOVE AND CARE

Friends are our chosen family,
in whose presence we feel at home.

Love is all that matters. It is the sharing of
songs and of silences only the heart can hear.

There is infinite wisdom in sharing the depths of your heart.

Friendships nurture our spirits and give us
the courage to follow our dreams.

Some people come into our lives and quickly go.
Some stay for a while, leave footprints
on our hearts, and we are never, ever, the same.

Care is the golden thread of friendship that
transcends all time and distance.

Faith

A
Understanding

In the company of true friendship, we shed our masks
and find the freedom to be ourselves.

With you, I wear no disguises. Thank you for the comfort
you bring and for loving me for who I am.

Comfort

Real friends are rare. We've shared tears,
hopes, and dreams, you and I. Lucky are we.

It's good to have someone like you in my life — someone
with whom I can share so much of me.

Some people hear the music we hear
and understand the sound of words unspoken.

A listening heart offers shelter from the storm.

POST
CARD

Sweet Remembrance

We remember our pleasures with fullness of heart.

I hope you know how much you are loved,
and how lucky the world is to have someone like you.

Reflection

You are so much a part of who I am, and I will always
cherish the many ways you've made my heart sing.

I give thanks for the *yesterdays* my heart still holds in its pockets.

Gratitude

Some meetings are fashioned by chance.
Surely ours was a gift of fate.

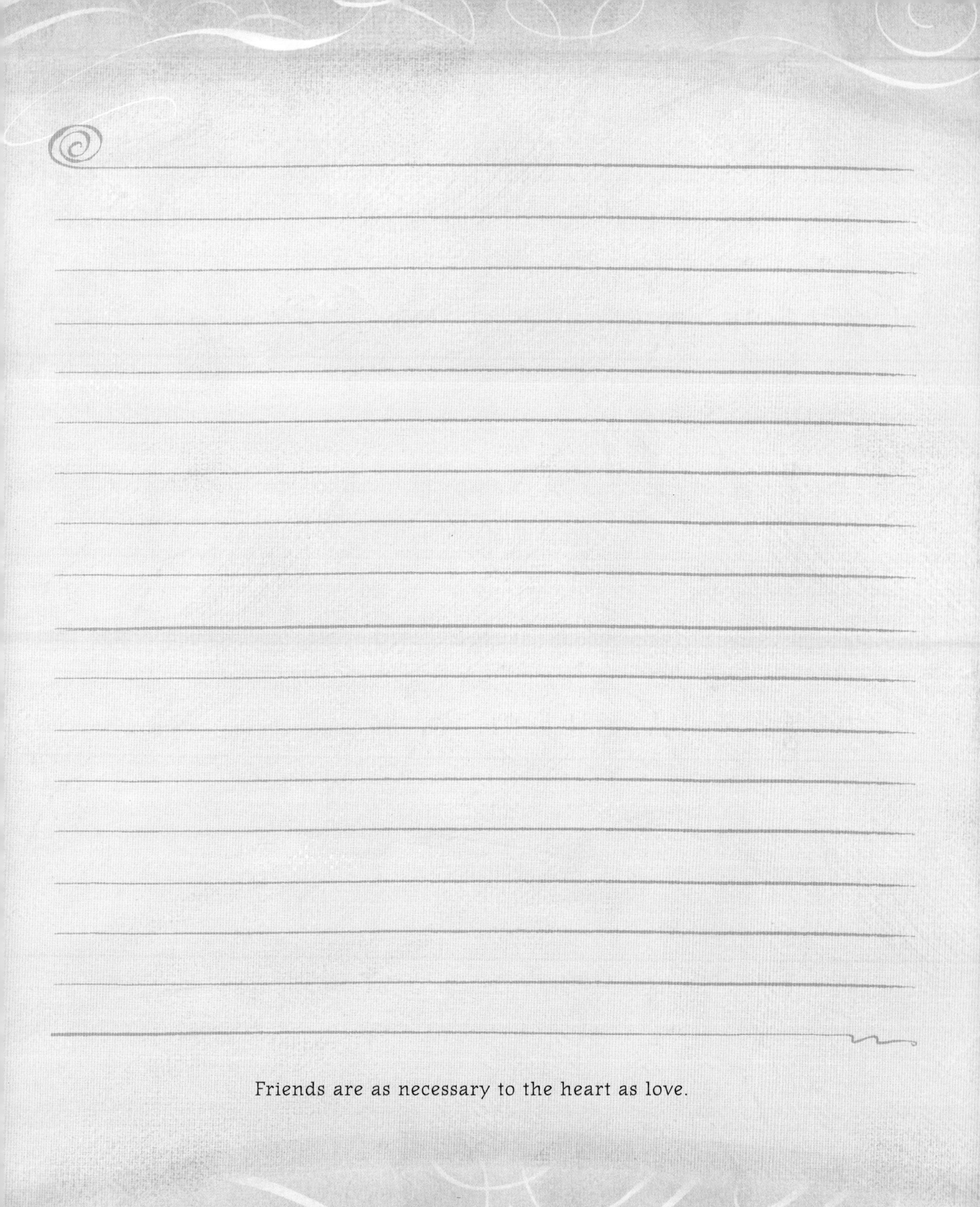

Friends are as necessary to the heart as love.

Friendship is a treasured gift to the soul.

Time never takes the precious things away.
Real friends are forever.

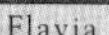

Flavia

Photos by Chris Chandler

Lisa and her daughter Sylvie

Flavia Weedn is one of America's leading inspirational writers and illustrators. Her work, and the work of her daughter and co-author, Lisa Weedn, celebrates life and offers hope to the human spirit.

Their collaborative work has touched the lives of millions through books, cards, posters, fine stationery products, and hundreds of licensed goods throughout the world.

Flavia and Lisa live in Santa Barbara, California.